Little Sparks of Joy

Dear Fiona

May the colours, the elements
of Mother Earth and
the uplifting poetry in this book
ignite Little Sparks of JOY
in your life
and blessings
in your new beginnings!
Love & Light

Little Sparks of Joy

Messages from across the globe
igniting **H**ope, **L**ove, **U**nity and **J**oy

in association with the

RAINBOW Letters to Mother Earth Project

First published and distributed in the United Kingdom by:
Golden Muse Publishing, Nantwich, Cheshire, CW5
Tel: +44 (0)77 6605 2060; In association with
www.rainbowletterstomotherearth.com

The information given in this book should not be treated as a substitute for professional medical advice; always consult a medical practitioner. Any use of information in this book is at the reader's discretion and risk. Neither the author nor the publisher can be held responsible for any loss, claim, or damage arising out of the use, or misuse, of the suggestions made, or the failure to take medical advice.

Golden Muse Publishing does not have any control over, or any responsibility for, any author or third-party websites referred to in or on this book.

A catalogue record for this book is available from the British Library.

ISBN: 978-1-9164664-1-8

Editor: Susan Brookes Morris
Co-editor: ChriSOULa Sirigou
Book producer: Samantha Houghton
Book Cover Artwork "Mama Earth" by K8 the heARTist, Kate Lumley

Printed in the United Kingdom

Visit: www.rainbowletterstomotherearth.com to find features, educational resources, book contributors' interviews and news of upcoming events, and you can sign up for e-newsletters so that you're always first to hear about our upcoming callouts and collaborative projects.

To all joy bringers.

To my sister, Maria, who says yes to joy even in the darkest moments.

To my father-in-law who believed in me.

"Giggle" — K8 the heARTist, USA

Contents

Foreword... 10

Preface... 15

Introduction... 16

RAINBOW Letters to Mother Earth............................. 19

Mother Earth, mOMma Gaia™............................... 22

Rainbow me is RAINBOW YOU 24

Life's Gift 25

Imagination and Joy... 26

Curiosity and Joy.. 28

The Call of Mama Gaia.. 30

Healing Art.. 33

Discovering Joy Through Change............................. 34

Poetry and Joy.. 37

A Letter to Mother Earth...................................... 39

As Our World Goes, We Go................................... 40

Today's Gift From Heaven Above.............................. 43

Dear Mother Earth.. 44

Rainbow.. 46

I walked towards the Forest....................................47

Rainbow Letter to Mother Earth.......................51

At the Edge of the Rainbow............................. 53

Στην άκρη του ουράνιου τόξου........................ 56

Ocean.. 59

A Greater Cause... 61

Worth, Mojebu and the Is-ness........................62

A Love Letter To My Mother Gaia {Mother Earth}.......................71

Dear Gaia.. 72

Gratitude: A Way of Life.................................. 74

Multi-lingual Messages of Gratitude and Joy............................. 75

Fimleikar!... 78

Gymnastics!... 78

Owning what has always been mine................. 79

Dear Mother Earth.. 80

Rainbow Recipe for Joy................................... 82

Your powerful inner light................................. 84

Cosmic Connections..86

Goddess from Epona.......................................89

My A-Z of JOY..90

Resources..92

Epilogue..96

About ChriSOULa...99

Acknowledgements..101

Photo and Image Credits...............................103

What next?..104

Get Creative...105

Write your RAINBOW Letter........................105

Testimonials & Endorsements......................107

Foreword

In this life, I have learned a great deal about human beings from all over our precious planet. I have learned that there are in fact 8 billion worlds going on all at the same time and that each one of us has our own world to care for and love.

When we do this very thing – love and care for our individual planet and world we have – we begin to create a shared world of love and it is this very love in our hearts that heals the world and brings it back together again as one.

Our beautiful, beautiful blue jewel, Mother Earth – thank you for not giving up on us and for having faith that we are able to love you the way you deserve to be loved.

What I know for sure, each one of us manages our fears as best we can and each one of us tries to celebrate our loves and our successes as best we can and I know Mother Earth knows this.

When ChriSOULa asked me to write the Foreward to this book I really wasn't sure I was the one cut out for the job. Of course humbled and grateful to be asked, I wasn't sure I was worthy or able to do this with the grace this book genuinely deserves.

You see, I wasn't sure I could personally feel the joy in 2020 that exists in the title of this precious book and give the appropriate foreward to a dedicated group of people who genuinely care for this gorgeous world that I so dearly love and hold so close to my heart and soul until today – and with tears in my eyes while typing this on my Macbook Pro – when I actually took the time to finally read this book I knew instantly I was home and that I was the soul destined to do this for us all.

While reading the words in this manuscript, Earth started to whisper to my heart with the whales, with the trees, with the many forests and the many songs I have written to help Mother Earth over the years to give her a voice to communicate with human beings as best I can through the music I write, channel, and sing in service to humanity. And while reading one of the poems in this book the smell of pure fresh air and nourishing oxygen from the rainforest in Tofino British Columbia Canada began to circle my presence and awareness. As I read more of the beautiful letters to mother earth the whales started to show me that it's why they recently jumped for joy when I was out to visit them on Vancouver Island in Canada last month.

This book is loaded with the intelligence and emotional empathy, care, compassion and integrity that it will take for all of us to start new conversations about what we can do as human beings and how we are able to unite our love together again from all of our hearts and souls for Mother Earth bringing her back together again with our love – not later but right here, right now and to take action by uniting in grassroots projects like this one that can actually reach the hearts and souls that genuinely care for our world of one love expanding one love in divine service.

One of the messages that came clearly through my heart and soul is to begin this precious book with two conscious songs that I sang at the United Nations Headquarters in New York City in 2017 – while sharing the stage with the incredible Dr. Bruce Lipton as well as a beautifully kind Brahma Kumaris Sister – Sister BK Shivani who flew in from India. The event was moderated by my dear friend Denis Scotto and together we held space for our precious planet with divine love.

The 1st song I would like to dedicate to you is called "I Believe In You."

This song begins with a short reflective oceanic meditation and continues to support you with divine pure love.

The 2nd song I would like to dedicate to you is called "The Miracle of You."

This song is all about going within and taking a journey to paradise from inside your heart and soul.

What I know for sure is that these letters to mother earth are beautiful and what this book so clearly illustrates is that we are all able to write our own letter to mother earth realizing and remembering we are all one love with pure peace.

Ultimately, a wise heart and soul knows that the world changes when we change and this book shows the process of that very organic nature and original light that each of us has within us.

May we all unite our hearts and souls together again and walk home to the promised land of pure love shared among us all taking care of this precious Mother that houses us all and let us all do it with as much joy as possible!

— Dr. Rev. Paul Luftenegger, D.Min.
International Multi Award Winning Conscious
Singer/Songwriter/Composer
Inspiring Global Love & Kindness From Within

"I BELIEVE IN YOU"

Music & Lyrics By Paul Luftenegger © 2016 All Rights Reserved Performed at the United Nations Headquarters in New York City in 2017 Sharing the Stage with Dr. Bruce Lipton PhD & Sister Shivani of the Brahma Kumaris of India.

We are one world of love
We are the Universal love
We must teach the children it's all about the love
We must model and lead this world with all our love

Oh, I believe, I believe, I believe, in you

Oh, stop and look up at the pretty skies of blue
Smell the fragrant flowers they are growing for you
And watch the sunset upon the oceans
See the stars fill up the skies at night
And find the rainbows that are yours
The Universe is full of treasure just for you

Oh, I believe
I believe, I believe in you

Oh, help the endangered species
They need our help
Oh, help our precious, precious planet
Cradle the earth with your heart
And love yourself love yourself
And love your neighbours
Brothers and sisters that's who we are
And find the rainbows that are yours
The Universe is full of treasure just for you

And I know I cannot do this on my own
I'm not big enough to do this life alone
I know need all the help, all the help that I can get
That's why I'm calling at the angels and the saints of love
Because I believe in expanding the love
And I've learned that if you get lost and scared along the way
You must always know that the love in your heart
Will be the light that guides you home

Because I know In my heart
That you're an angel, that's who you are
Because I believe in you

Preface

The book you connect with is a collection of poems, stories, artwork, and messages of gratitude from authors and illustrators from across the globe. Each of them has opened up their heart to bring you insight into their intimate connection with Mother Earth and how they allow beauty, joy and light into their present lives.

Because our authors are from a variety of countries and we are publishing these poems and stories in English you may notice that the spelling of the words is sometimes in British English and sometimes in American English, depending on the authors' country of origin. You'll also see that some phrases they use seem unusual to you, as there are not always direct translations.

In light of the fact that the youngest of our authors is seven years old and many of our authors are not native English speakers, our team of editors has worked hard to make each story, poem and contribution clear and full of the impact the author intended. It is our sincere hope that we have done justice to their messages of gratitude and love letters to Mother Earth and that you will be moved and inspired by them.

If you'd like to hear the authors - children, young people and adults - in their own voice and watch or listen as they provide context and colour to how they decided that this was the time to share their Little Sparks of Joy for the betterment of the whole, I invite you to visit www.RainbowLettersToMotherEarth.com to watch or listen to interviews with them, conducted by the book's publisher, ChriSOULa Sirigou.

Introduction

As light bearers and joy bringers we need good information, to step through our fears and to take the right actions for ourselves, our community and our environment. I really hope this extremely important book will help the Rainbow warrior within you to rise.

I believe it is time for us to consider a radical new view of health and healing that recognises the truth that not only does "all life breathe together", we also "co-create together." And those acts of co-creation include the health and well-being of our collective psychic – and physical – health as well as the health of the ecological system.

For years we have been inspired by the thought that, "We co-create our own reality." We apply that truth to our health all the time now, examining

what negative thought forms might be influencing our illnesses. And then we turn to positive thoughts as a way of promoting our health. But I realised quite some time ago that our thoughts and emotions are participating in micro and macro acts of co-creation constantly, not just in terms of our health. We are living engines of co-creation. Our thoughts and our choices and our actions are continually blending into the greater pool of everyone's energy, creating the events that happen in the world around us.

We are indeed the engines behind all that is created. It may well be that our "inner climate" is energetically connected to the collective climate of this planet. Climate change is due to many factors, just as our health and well-being relies upon many components. Many of these are obvious, such as lifestyle habits. Likewise, many of the causes of climate change are obvious, such as pollution, deforestation, fracking, and so on. But we are comprised of the same elements as the Earth. We are air, water, earth, and fire. Perhaps we need to consider the unimaginable: That there are no boundaries between our personal energy systems and all of nature. We are one great, interconnected field of life, comprised of air, earth, water and fire. Consciousness is a factor of energy, not form.

As the great spiritual masters taught: What is in One is in the Whole; As Above, So Below; What we do to one person, we do to everyone. Buddha also taught that what we see is an illusion. The truth requires emptying the soul of all that you thought was real. We have to "become empty" in order to see clearly for the first time.

Buddha said all is "nothing", meaning that what we think is permanent is nothing but an illusion. Everything is here but for a second and then gone. Even the trees you are looking at today are different tomorrow. Nothing is ever "the same". We may think that we exist separate from everyone else – but that is a great illusion, perhaps the greatest one of all.

Carl G. Jung described the collective unconscious as this domain of archetypal patterns that influence the collective psyche of humankind. All of us share these patterns because we are all a part of the collective human experience.

These mystical teachings that Jesus and Buddha and other masters spoke of to their students need to be examined once again but within the context of how we understand the power of human consciousness today and the realisation we have awakened to that is: We do, in fact, co-create our reality.

But that reality extends far beyond our personal health. It's time we take the radical leap in thinking – and in imagining – and realise that if we co-create our personal health, we must also be participating in the creation of the health of the whole planetary ecological system. It is time we think in terms of a bio-spiritual-ecology in which we truly understand that:

- All is One – but how do we live that?
- All Life Breathes Together – how do we actually experience that truth?
- What I do to one person, I do to everyone
- Every choice I make to heal myself helps to heal the whole
- Collective illnesses and epidemics are exactly that: collective illnesses
- Psychic illnesses are real
- Energetic disorders are real – and felt by individuals. Is your depression really "your" depression or are you picking up the depression in the collective?
- How do your personal actions influence the whole?
- What is our relationship to climate change?
- What are the ways we can heal our self and the whole?
- How we need to understand health according to the mystical laws that govern creation

"We are the engines of climate change. It is not happening around us; it is happening through us, in us and because of us."

Bio-spiritual-ecology is a new way of approaching health; in fact, of understand the way we co-create our shared reality. Co-creation is all about how we direct energy and energy does not have boundaries, like physical matter does. All of our energy systems in some way merge and blend with all the energies of life. We are all responsible for the quality of all life on this planet – yours, mine, and all of Nature.

It's time we start perceiving our capacity to co-create through micro-and macro lenses, for the truth is: What is in One is indeed in the Whole. We can heal this planet – one person at a time. And it starts with us.

RAINBOW Letters to Mother Earth

We know the truth about Climate Change.

Cancer, autoimmune diseases, Alzheimer's, as well as depression, anxiety, arthritis, heart disease, autism, sleep and eating disorders, obesity, and more are on the rise.
Millions are suffering each day.
Millions are on a desperate search for answers…

What if … the answers come from our children and young people?
What if … the response comes from us, change makers, who believe that change comes from within.
What if … the answer lies in saying Yes to being kind to oneself, to the planet and others and to helping co-create a culture of compassion in action, togetherness and kindness in families, schools and wider communities?

RAINBOW Letters to Mother Earth community project responds to this multifaceted crisis. Our core mission and vision are Youth Engagement and Unite in Harmony.

We invite RAINBOW Warriors Protectors from all over the world to respond to this calling through writing love letters to/or from the Earth, future or past generations, those who hold positions of power and influence, or other species. The idea is open to interpretation: it could come from a personal place, be dramatic in form, be a call to action. The invitation is open to all - youth, grown ups and elders. This is an opportunity to pause; to ask how this existential threat affects the way we wish to live our lives and the compassion in action we take.

So far individuals, families and schools have responded globally from Cyprus, Canada, Denmark, England, Germany, Greece, Hawaii, Iceland, Indonesia, Italy, Netherlands, Scotland, South Africa and USA.

Poets, illustrators and writers of various cultures, ethnicities and age groups, express their love, appreciation, admiration and gratitude towards Mother Earth through words, colour, lyrics, rhythm and light. Equally, emotions like fear, grief, anger, frustration, worry, anxiety, doubt, insecurity are expressed in their RAINBOW Letters, Poems and Artwork with a shared purpose to incentivise our core need to safeguard our home, Planet Earth, create better relationships and opportunities for the young generation to grow equally, peacefully and wholeheartedly.

— **ChriSOULa Sirigou, Founder,**
RAINBOW Letters to Mother Earth Project

Be gentle with yourself
and others

"May Sparks of Love and Light Take Flight Around the 7 Seas"

"Giving Birth to the New Earth
An Earth with 7 Cs;
Compassion, Courage, Creativity, Communication,
Connection, Collaboration and Contribution.
Living the Way of the Heart
For Love is who we Are"

— Anna Sophia, Netherlands

Mother Earth,
mOMma Gaia™

It is with gr8 enthusiasm that I AM pARTicipating in this compilation of LOVE offerings to Mother eARTh. It so reson8es with my heART. I AM all about the ART that dWELLs within each of us being DRAWn out to PAINT a bigger picture of how incredibly beautiful life can be.

As a visionary artist using my ART & my heART to bring about gr8er LOVE & EWEnity consciousness in our world a WHOLE new EWEnIverse® is being born. It is called EWEtopIa®- at its core it represents the PLAYce in our consciousness wHERE consciousness challenges are reSOLVEd, and BEings are choosing to live in LOVE over FEAR and living sovereignly vs. sheepishly. This Journey began for me with the LOVE EWES® in 2014 starting to show themselves to me in FUN energy WAYS. I later learned by being with this MAGICal cast of characters that they lived on the Fun "e" (energy) Farm™ and had so many Fun "e" Friends™. They all have gr8 wisdOM and tales to share. These tales are currently in development into books, soundtracks, films, cartoons, curriculum and more. In Rainbow Letters to Mother Earth, Little Sparks of Joy, I share several of them with you on the book's cover.

Mother Earth, mOMma Gaia™, holds creatures GR-8 & smALL and knows each of their importance and value. ALL is inside the word smALL. ALL LIVES play their pART in our ONEderFULL experience of being alive 2gather. Like all nurturing mothers, she teaches us each HOW GR8 thou heART and the value of caring for ourselves and one another.

The "EWE" in mOMma Gaia's™ arms represents each YOU on our "PLAN-IT" stepping out of fear and "sheeparation" & into BEing the LOVE that YOU ARE.

DAY-SEE™, the FLOW-er, represents our plant friends and shares her important message that our gr8est DAYS will NOW & ALL WAYS be SEEn when LOVE & LAUGHTER are the FLOW-ers.

In mOMma Gaia's™ hand sEWEper pALLin8or™, the HUM-ble bee of EWEtopIa®, may be seen elevated along the side of the MATCH-ic stick of INSPIR8-I,ON™.

sEWEper pALLin8or™, has a powerful message to share, No matter how small you may be, you have a voice and matter. He inspires the expansion of love & kindness by pollinating his LIGHT all over the PLAYce. The words of his GOLD-IN™ hit songs drip honey & open the heART to enable one's SWEETest LIFE to alchemically be created. The love his songs share STICKs with the listener long after the lyrics end. This wise old SOUL inner-stands that GLOW-bALL PEACE™ begins, when each BEing is being their PEACE. He appears again in this book, on pages illustrating the lyrics to one of the songs, by Paul Luftenegger. Paul is the Being that brings this magical creature to life with his beautiful voice and essence.

The MATCH-ic STICK of INSPIR8-I,ON™, reflects the SPARK of JOY that one FEELS when they are in alignment with their true Divine nature. I hope that my heART SPARKS JOY in EWEr heART.

— K8 the heARTist, USA

RAINBOW **ME** IS RAINBOW **YOU**

WE
ARE EVERY SINGLE
COLOR

WE
ARE EVERY SINGLE
HUE

BEING
OUR OWN
COLORS

IS
ALL WE
NEED TO DO,

TO CHANGE THE WORLD
TOGETHER

WE
JUST NEED EVERY
HUE
THATS EVERY SINGLE
YOU

Poem for the Rainbow Poems for Mother Earth

Resplendently Yours,

Jessycka Drew Colors

Nationality: All Nations

Current Incarnation Location: East Coast USA

Consent to share in any media capacity both print, online, and spoken word for every
word of for every one

ALL ONE ALL

Signed: Jessycka Drew Colors

Life's gift

Life itself is a gift
Breathing in a conscious way
Exploring a realm beyond words.
Singing out a song of sounds
with the voice of my soul
Dancing to the rhythm
with the music of my spirit.

Some actions we love immediately,
Others are complicated to accept.
Breathe, think and act
In a conscious and connected way
Encounter the most precious gift of life,
The Acceptance of What Is.

— Viola Edward de Glanville,
July 2001, Cyprus

Imagination and Joy

Joy is always present or at least available. When we don't feel it or see it, it's because we are choosing to focus on something else. This is understandable in many circumstances. There are times of sadness, disappointment, anger and frustration, but we don't have to stay there, we do have choice. We can change our 'mind.' This is simple, but I know it's not always easy to change our focus and thoughts. Rather than focus too much on the loss of a loved one for example, be grateful for knowing them, think of the good times. Rather than focusing on what you haven't got, be grateful for all the things you do have. Gratitude is a great way to raise your vibration and help you feel joy.

We literally do have a spark in our brain when we have a thought, the neuron fires up and sparks across a gap, a synapse and connects to another neuron. When we have the same thought over and over again we strengthen the firing of those neurons. So have good, happy, joyful thoughts. Thoughts become things and attract more of the same.

The body doesn't know the difference between our imagination and the 'real' thing. Imagine biting into or eating a raw lemon, when you spend a few minutes really imagining this, the body responds as though you are really doing it and your mouth starts to water. Your imagination is a very powerful thing. Let it take you to a favourite place, or make one up, imagine it, where everything is as you would love it to be. You start to feel it in the body, you vibrate at the frequency of it and start to attract it, or things of a similar vibration into your life. It is a great way of relaxing, de-stressing, lowering anxiety and feeling good.

Using the imagination is especially helpful for children. Especially when they are stuck inside and not able to go out. We can use our imagination to create whatever we want, wherever we want. With younger children, even on a routine car journey, maybe on the way to school, ask where they are going today and come up with as many different places as you can. You suggest and let their imagination run wild.

They could be going to Africa on a safari where they'll see and think about all the different animals, they might encounter. Or the South Pole where they'll live in an Igloo. Ask them, what they might see and do there? They could go to the moon in a rocket, passing stars and galaxies. What else might they see? Or, to Venice and travel on a gondola, eat ice cream and sing opera. In America, they could visit the Statue of Liberty, go inside and climb up to the top.

You can do this kind of thing indoors and enhance the activity by building trains, planes, boats, rocket ships U.F.O.s out of anything you have. You could make Igloos, tents, Wigwams and caves with no more than a sheet over chairs. You need only provide basic items and their imagination will do the rest.

Rather than restrict them, encourage them. Let them blossom. This use of imagination is good for the brain, it fires neurons off that help create ways of thinking and habits that are beneficial to them, in all areas of learning and life.

— **Karen Shaw, UK**

Curiosity and Joy

Drawn by the precious metal, jewellery design and the casting process, Alex followed his curiosity and made his own unique silver ring.

The intuitive design process inspired him to use a wrench as the mould and to learn the silversmithing techniques of design, form preparation, melting, casting, cleaning, filing, and forming the ring. The ring continues to spark his curiosity and it changes every now and then when he feels inspired to file or sand it into new versions of 'Curiosity.'

What sparks your curiosity?

— Alex is from Denmark. He is 14 years old and was 11 when he created 'Curiosity' the ring.

The unique 'Curiosity' design including the pattern inside from the wrench.

So satisfying to see the silver melt under the furnace.

Shine bright forevermore my little star
To become brighter everyday
Seeing all of us becoming greater beings of true purpose
Brings tears of joy
To witness for what we have forgotten
And now we are awake
And waking others like the rainbows
Sparkling with life
Shine on my beautiful star

— Richard Dubrick, Canada

The Call of Mama Gaia

I was on a walk out with the dogs and found a flower broken off, but still connected with the second half of the stem and still with roots..I decided to take it home, make a bandage to support and stabilise the broken bit and plant it in the earth.

Masuro Emoto inspired me to put wee notes and messages written on paper in the ground, telling the plant that I love her and how beautiful she is, to encourage her to heal, believe in herself and that everything is possible!

Now, this plant has not only recovered, she is in full bloom a second time and looks so vibrant and proud. I tell her that I love her every time I pass her and I kiss her. I feel her enthusiasm about her own recovery and her love and gratitude towards me. It is just one of the wonders and miracles presented every day to me.

I love walking barefoot and last year managed to continue this right until the middle of December. I then started again in the middle of March. I just love the enjoyment of taking my shoes off when most would think it too cold to do so, but I do, because I want to cross the river to take a short cut to the beach.

Three years ago, I started barefoot running and this is so great through all seasons of course. Although I have to confess, it can be a wee bit painful in the beginning, but the whole effect on your mood and your connectedness to earth is what counts !!!

Ten days ago, I felt guided, to think about moving into a tent, to be closer to Mama Gaia and the beauty she has to offer. I followed that call and put up a tent in the garden, seven days ago. What I experienced through that, is making me feel so passionate about the fact that I live and breathe and coexist with all these wonderful creations. It makes me also feel safe, so loved, so welcome, so held.

I live in Scotland and with the long, light nights what I am witnessing is a huge, impressive spectacle in itself. I see the sky changing, preparing itself, before the sun appears on the scene, in colours and tones we also know from the rainbow, from blue, light green and yellowish to turning into pink, orange yellowish, then to white yellowish with all the rainbow colours shining and radiating in each ray.

The first four nights I slept with an open tent, I saw the sky and stars. I could hear the sea, the birds, geese, crows, pigeons, magpies, swans, robins, sparrows, starlings, butterflies, bees and bumble bees. It was pure delight. The fifth night I had to spend in the house, because it was too stormy and the tent started to become leaky, what a change this was, a sort of disconnectedness.

How far we have come as human beings in some ways, but in building houses, I imagine, there is still much more that is possible in terms of being and staying more in contact and exchanging with the Mother. Also, in terms of our heath, it's definitely not one of my desires to live in a well-isolated and insular house, where you feel only numb and separate from life itself and the pulse of nature.

What was becoming clear whilst I was writing this was that I would send this 'article' to the 'Rainbow letters to Mother Earth.' You, as a reader now know how passionate I am about being on and with the Mother. I believe, that to keep her in that beauty, it might be extremely relevant to treat this pulsing, nurturing creature on which we live with love and respect N O W

— **Gabriele Wolter, Scotland**

Healing Art

- A therapeutic way to create beauty
out of any situation.

Dedicating my Angel Art to the world, in the hopes that she will inspire you to create something beautiful.

I lost my Grandma recently under extraordinary conditions. I chose to color and celebrate her life, rather than fall apart.

Dear Grandma, as the doctors and nurses keep you comfortable, I hold you close to my heart. I color wellsprings of joy, offering prayers of remembrance – I see you only in your light, your innocence, filled with astonishing grace.

I honor your strength and your ability to hold your head high, with true dignity and respect.

I pray for your angels to greet you when you gently release, and as your golden wings take flight, may our hearts hold together forever in no time, as you fly sweetly into God's Colorful Rainbow.

I love you sweet Grandma, I love you.

— **Sharon Mundy, USA**

Discovering Joy Through Change

Back in 2010 I literally lay on the kitchen floor sobbing. I'd had to move into a rented house after my marriage break up. I was struggling with the change and trying to maintain some sense of normality for my two daughters who were 1 and 4 years old at the time. I was just about dealing with my divorce, but then my hugely successful business hit horrific, turbulence and before I knew it too, came crashing down around me. I went from having more money than I knew how to handle, to bailiffs knocking on my door and taking my car away!

My work and my babies were my life and I felt like I had failed - failed at my marriage, failed as a mother and failed at business. I just wanted to hide under my duvet and never come out again, but I had to find a way. My girls needed me! I needed me!

The rug had been pulled from under me, the ground felt so rocky. But one step at a time I discovered some fabulous techniques, which I went on to develop, helping me to get through all the loss, grief and turmoil that life has presented me with.

No matter how rocky the ground you are standing on, how fragile you feel, take these baby steps forward to re-discover your joy, by living in the moment and experiencing the beauty around you.

STEPPING STRIPES:

Step 1 Grab yourself a notebook, a red and a green pen.

Step 2 Each day in red write all the things you're struggling with - the negativity and pain. In green write anything positive that has happened, it may be as small as a bird landing in the garden or your child smiling at you. Make this a daily practice.

Step 3 When you look back you will just see how far you have come.

FOCUSSING ON DOING SMALL THINGS WITH GREAT LOVE:

- Plant a seed, nurture it and watch it grow
- Study a flower in your home daily, watch it open and bloom
- Write yourself a note and stick it on your mirror "Today 'your name' you have got this!"
- Activate something in your home that makes you feel joyful. Candles are fabulous for this as you can actively 'light up your joy' as you ignite the flame.

And always, know that in life we have to experience the dark to enjoy the light.

— **Naomi Victoria Gilmour, UK**

Blooming Angel — by Sabine Rixen, Netherlands

Poetry and Joy

**'Words carry with them energy, medicine.'
— Meggan Watterson**

Since the lockdown began and my intention was set to bring forth RAINBOW Letters to Mother Earth, I've read the observation a few times, that many people are looking to poetry to try to make sense of these extraordinary times we're living in. The deep insight that poetry can express in a way that prose struggles to distil has enabled it to be a source of wisdom and deep reflection amid all the 'information' we're bombarded with online.

I was struck by W. H. Auden's observation, 'Poetry is the only art people haven't yet learnt to consume like soup.' This describes the preciousness of poetry for many people who seek self-expression and to embody love through poetic form.

In addition, Robert Holden has said, 'I didn't have much time for poetry when I was young. Maybe I was in too much of a hurry. . . Fortunately for me, one poem after another found their way through my defences and came to my rescue. Slowly, but surely, I began to see that inside each poem there was a gift waiting for me. A gift to help open up something inside of me—a new awareness, an epiphany, a cure for loneliness, renewed courage, and a call to action.'

Little Sparks of Joy offers that same gift to you in a luminous collection of original poetry set from a selection of poets across the globe. The poems in these pages 'are meditations with lyrics', and they invite you on a journey that will awaken the awareness of love's presence all around you.

Poems can often work like angels. They find you when you most need them. They bring comfort. Some poems become lifelong friends. You turn to them when you need good company. They help you to pay attention to your life. They encourage you to stay faithful to yourself and have faith in life.

— ChriSOULa Sirigou, UK

A Letter to Mother Earth

Our beloved Mother Earth, The Mother of all mothers! Beautiful and loving Gaia.

Thank you for giving us magnificent Nature with glorious mountains, hills, savannas and deserts.

I want to express my gratitude for evergreen forests with oxygen providing trees so we can breathe easily.

Thank you for beautiful emerald oceans, seas and rivers shimmering in the sunshine like a glowing gold on the turquoise scarf allowed to fly high up to the sky.

Thank you for all the creatures, big and small, silk-skinned, feathered and furry, no-legged, 2-legged and 4-legged, awesome animals, funny grasshoppers, scary alligators, royal lions and dogs who wiggle happy tails.

Thank you for all those colourful birds and common ones! They all bring so much joy with their beautiful singing and so much fun with their cheerful tweeting.

Thank you for giving us drinking water that I have unrestricted access to everyday. Many human beings do not have it, suffering thirst and hunger. This is definitely something which the New Era of our earthy life after the virus will find a solution to.

Thank you, Mother Earth, for fresh fruits and vegetables that are extremely necessary in our diet and beneficial for our health. They are delicious when eaten raw or cooked, full of vitamins and minerals.

Thank you for the variety of beans, nuts, barley, other seeds and wheat, so we can bake homemade bread with love and other good stuff like cookies and cakes.

I'm profoundly grateful having been given a chance to be one of your habitants.

There is nothing more comforting like bare-foot stepping on your surface and feeling your heart pulsating underneath my feet. I do that so happily when watering flowers in our garden and watching them blossom.

I promise to always love you, respect you and care for you, living in a harmony with myself and other co-inhabitants.

Thank you for being my Home and my Secret Garden which my family loves as much as I do.

— **Gaja Lesiak (9 years) and grandmother, Mira, UK**

As Our World Goes, We Go

The plankton are dying
Plastics inside
Kill and mame
Our shame our blame

It is we who will die
By our own demise
Our greed our laziness
Polluting oceans and skies

We talk and talk
We don't walk the walk
Massive explosions
Fracking and erosions

Torturing our earth
Tunnels give birth
Destroying our foundation
Pervasive mutations

Lack of humanity
Insanity thrives
In the quest for greed
Power over mankind

Awaken and see
Your killing our seas
From beautiful whales
To sharks with no tails

Just to satisfy a hunger
That money can buy
Money won't buy life
When birds no longer fly

When bees no longer buzz
When Nothing is done in love
When water has been poisoned
When corn cannot be digested

Diseases start to spread
Toxins of chemicals and lead
Permeating our food supply
More and more begin to die

What will it take
More than our lives at stake
Yet we argue and fuss
Over such trivial stuff

Wake up Wake up
Together together
Hand in hand
Forever

Is the only way
Our planet survives
Our animals thrive
Our neighbours stay alive

It starts with our oceans
Connecting us all
The world we live in
Should not have walls

Love is needed
Across the globe
Love has been depleted
So let's help love grow

Hand in hand we must unite
From country to country
From land and sea
No boundaries dividing

With effort
With action
With thought
We win!

Stop fighting and crying
Nothing will get resolved
No time left for egos
No time left

No time left

With passion we come together
With heart we care
With energy we surge
With strength we rise

With Love We Survive

— @ kcgloer 2020

Today's Gift From Heaven Above

I pulled back the curtains and there it graced the sky - a beautiful, beautiful rainbow, a celebration before my eyes

My heart vibrating in such a delight of Joy as I looked and said - Oh boy!

I know a rainbow happens when God wishes us to see his gifts and to listen and to Just Be

A rainbow brings Joy to us and a promise to behold.

When a rainbow is painted in the sky it is Mother Earth singing her beautiful colorful song.

That everything is going to be ok if we take a Pause and BE

We breathe and feel rainbow colors on our head and as we breathe and feel rainbow colors in our hair, we can find the piece of peace.

Oh, beautiful rainbow I breathe all of you in and know that this is a sign from above to tell the world that this unity of colors makes such a magical sight.

As you fill the sky with colors and with hope, for us to dance and sing with Joy under these seven rays of color, for us to feel free and to feel the love from above.

For us to know our dreams will come true and a pot of gold awaits, just for you.

So go today and breathe and BE all you can be and shine like a Rainbow Warrior of Light and know this gift came for you today, to open you up so you can shine more light into Mother Earth and smile your Rainbow Smile into our beloved earth.

Please believe this rainbow came to heal us all and show us unity and consciousness.

So tonight, when you lay your head on your pillow, may you see your rainbow etched on your soul, and sleep with a Rainbow Smile from above, and as you sleep, send rainbow blessings for peace into our beloved Earth Mother.

Namaste

— **Elspeth Kerr, Cyprus**

Dear Mother Earth

It is June now. It is so beautiful in the rainforest in West Kalimantan. Not too hot, not too dry. The rain comes almost every afternoon. Sometimes it is a light rain, and I can play hide and seek with cousins. Sometimes we play chasing, or we just play jumping up and down in muddy puddles. Or we just swing from one tree to another..." Yuuppyyy" .... But sometimes, heavy rain comes with thunder and lightning.... a bit scary. But when it comes, we just gather under big trees. After the rain, in the morning, the rainforest is always a pleasant place .... the fresh smell, the clean air.

After June, it will be July, then August, then September....... I hate August. I hate September. Bad things happen in my rainforest. The sun begins to disappear as the sky fills with smoke. My home the forest is set on fire and my lungs burn with the smoke I inhale. My eyes cry tears to keep the soot out of my eyes and my heart cries for the world. I see my friends, the monkeys, the birds, the snakes and all the little insects suffering because the human people are burning down our home. When that happens, I say to myself, why is this happening to this beauty of nature, the lungs of this earth that we all share. When will it stop?

Dear Mother Earth, I have a human friend called Khalida who lives in the big city nearby. During August and September, the burning season, she cannot go to school as her school is closed because of the smoke. The smoke, from my forest is too thick. She feels my pain too; she cries with me every year when they commit this crime of burning my home. Like other children in West Kalimantan, during that time, Khalida suffers breathing problems.

Please Mother Earth, help me. It is almost August, I don't want to struggle again this year, not knowing if my home will survive the flames and knowing that my friends will be in harm's way. Please help by showing these people who burn our forest to see how they are hurting my lungs, Khalida's lungs, and the world's lungs. I want us all to wake up to a clear sky and breathe freely, each and every day.

From the Rainforest, June 2020 - Orangutan

44

— Khalida Nur van Helden, Age 10, Indonesia

Rainbow

Glories from the refraction of a rainbow
Sunlight hitting raindrops causing multicoloured glow
Wavelengths increased from red to blue
The atmospheric cone with its rain bow hue.
Index of refraction disperses the colour
Vibrant with only a violet pallor
From an aeroplane the full circle is seen
From Earth the cone is just a dream
Seeing rainbows in our tears
Changing Hope from our Fears
Rainbows paint our lives with reflected light
Like water on leaves shining bright
Like diamonds skimming a deep blue sea
Rippling undulating shining free
Dew drops caught in a spider's web
So many dreams left unsaid.

— **Maureen Brindle, UK**

I walked towards the Forest

I walked towards the Forest
with longing, with love, with despair
I almost didn't go
My body was heavy
My mind was heavy
I almost couldn't find the strength to go
Even though I wanted to

I walked towards the Forest
Almost like a calling
My mind was aching
My tears were so close
I tried to keep myself together
Knowing that soon I'd get my release

I walked towards the Forest
And I already knew
My mind was cheering
My body was so excited
I felt the love of hands
From the forest reaching out
To me

I walked towards the Forest
It was coming closer and closer
I could hear it calling
I could hear it was waiting for me
My heart was pounding
My heart was calm
This moment just before entering
Always blows me away

I walked towards the Forest
And took the first step in
My eyes burst into tears
My heart felt at home
I could hear the voices of the Forest
Cheering happy with open arms
It was waiting for me
It was hugging me
It was healing me

I walked inside the Forest
Full of peace and serenity
I was so overwhelmed
Of all the love, strength and compassion
I fell in love
I always do
With the Forest, with myself

With the Forest in myself

I walked inside the Forest
And what always happens
Happened again
I felt so loved
I felt surrounded
As of family
As of friend
I felt at home
I felt safe
I felt strong
I felt understood
I felt belonging

I walked inside the Forest
Amazed at what it did to me
Again, and always
So good to me
I didn't understand
Why I so often struggled
To get up and get out
And into the Forest
When things hurt, overwhelm
Frustrate or drain my energy
Why the resistance
When I know it gives comfort?

I walked inside the Forest
And it said to me
That it was okay
It was alright
No one is perfect
We are perfect as we are
Walking in the Forest
Is always an acceptance
Of who I am
Utterly unconditionally

I walked home from the Forest
With a smile on my face

I felt recharged
I felt reborn
Gratitude and thankfulness
In body, mind and soul
Once again reminded
That I am never alone
The Forest helps me remember
Again, and again
That we are here together
That I am never alone

— Benedicte Holmbo Brandt, Denmark

Rainbow Letter to Mother Earth

During my whole life I have had this feeling that I belong to Mother Earth. Maybe we all are children from her. I think so.

Mother Earth gives me so much with her heart of rainbow colours and I love every one of them.

The RED one makes me think of LOVE – LOVE to our self, each other, plants and animals

The ORANGE one makes me think of PASSION

The YELLOW one makes me think of the SUN and the STARS who always guide me and make my DREAMS come through

The GREEN one makes me think of all the beautiful PLANTS and LIFE and makes me BELIEVE that we all together can save the planet earth

The BLUE one makes me think of the SEA and gives me the feeling of FREEDOM

The PURPLE one makes me think of MOTHER EARTH herself – it is just like a seed capsule that embraces all large and small ones.

I always feel safe with Mother Earth.

I love the adventures she tells me and I can always find the stories from her in my heart – I remember them especially if I am sad or I am sitting in school daydreaming.

We are always together to hear the birds singing.

We can feel the wind.

We can smell all the different scents and taste all the plants and berries, fruits and flowers.

Sometimes I just lie down, or when I'm swinging, I find small animals and build houses for them, make a cave in the trees or make a bonfire where all the flames dance and show us a kind of theatre.

Mother Earth gives me hope that we are all one world.

All together and I love that.

We have to take good care of Mother Earth because she gives our life magical experiences where we all can have fun and be exactly who we are.

— Filippa 10 years old, Denmark

At the Edge of the Rainbow

One early morning in December…

A grandfather and his five-year-old grandson were traveling north by train. The rest of the family was waiting for them to spend Christmas together. The little boy was travelling by train for the first time and did not hide his excitement. He climbed into the seat and stuck his head against the glass.

"Grandpa, grandpa, look at the sun behind the mountains!"

"It is a beautiful sunrise!" said the grandfather laughing.

"Grandpa, look at the mountains and the trees," he continued, commenting on what he was seeing.

"Look at the birds high in the sky," added the grandfather.

Then they crossed villages and cities. "Grandpa, look at the kids playing in their backyards!"

"Look at the people who work in the fields, the cars that go to the big city," added the grandfather.

It was noon and the little boy continued to be stuck to the glass, as he ate his sandwich. "Grandpa, grandpa, look how beautiful the clouds are. This is like a hare, yes, look, this is a horse, " he said, giving shapes to the cloudy sky.

Slowly the clouds merged, the shapes disappeared, and the sky darkened. Soon, thick drops hit the window loudly as the train kept on its way.

"Grandpa, I don't like the rain," the little boy complained. "It is getting dark. I cannot see anything! " The storm was now hitting the train window with intensity. The little boy was desperate, all nerves.

"Let's play something together," his grandfather begged him. "Bring your paintings."

"No, I do not want to. I want to be able to see outside. I do not like this small train carriage. "It's dark," he continued, grumbling.

"Yes, but this way we will reach your parents. Aren't you happy?"

"No! How will the time pass? Where are we?" he said, glued to the glass as he tried to look outside.

Frustrated with demanding something that was not happening, he fell asleep in his seat. A long time passed and at some point, he woke up and opened his eyes. The rain had stopped. Outside the window, the edge of a rainbow reached the train tracks.

"Grandpa, grandpa, look, a lot of colours", he got up shouting excitedly.

''They are following us!"

"Yes, my boy. These are the colours of the IRIS. We call it a rainbow!"

"Where were all these colours, Grandpa?" Why didn't we see them? "

"They were always here, my little boy. But it took rain to see them. It is the light that comes out through the drops of water".

"How beautiful it is, Grandpa."

Grandpa took him in his arms and looked him in the eyes. "So is our life, my little prince. Like the train route. We see beautiful pictures, we meet people and landscapes, but there are also storms. But never forget that a rainbow always comes after a storm. And hope returns to earth, as a promise for all the good that awaits us! "

"Yes, I will be home soon!" said the little one cheerfully. "I love you grandpa!"

— **Evniki Saatsaki, Greece**

Στην άκρη του ουράνιου τόξου

Κάποιο ξημέρωμα μιας μέρας του Δεκέμβρη...

Ένας παππούς με το πεντάχρονο εγγόνι του ταξίδευαν με το τρένο προς τον βορρά. Τους περίμενε η υπόλοιπη οικογένεια να περάσουν μαζί τα Χριστούγεννα.

Ο μικρός ταξίδευε πρώτη φορά με τρένο και δεν έκρυβε τον ενθουσιασμό του. Ανέβηκε στο κάθισμα και κόλλησε το κεφαλάκι του στο τζάμι.

«Παππού, παππού, κοίτα τον ήλιο πίσω από τα βουνά!».

«Είναι μια όμορφη ανατολή!» είπε γελώντας ο παππούς.

«Παππού, κοίτα τα βουνά και τα δένδρα», συνέχισε να σχολιάζει ό,τι έβλεπε ο εγγονός.

«Κοίτα τα πουλιά ψηλά στον ουρανό», συμπλήρωσε ο παππούς.

Έπειτα διέσχιζαν χωριά και πόλεις.

«Παππού, κοίτα τα παιδάκια που παίζουν στις αυλές τους!».

«Κοίτα τους ανθρώπους που δουλεύουν στα χωράφια, τα αυτοκίνητα που πάνε στη μεγάλη πόλη», πρόσθετε ο παππούς.

Έφτασε το μεσημέρι και ο μικρός συνέχισε να είναι κολλημένος στο τζάμι, τρώγοντας ένα σάντουιτς.

«Παππού, παππού, κοίτα τι όμορφα είναι τα σύννεφα. Αυτό είναι σα λαγός, να, κοίτα, αυτό είναι άλογο», έλεγε, δίνοντας σχήματα στον συννεφιασμένο ουρανό.

Σιγά-σιγά τα σύννεφα ενώθηκαν, τα σχήματα χαθήκαν και ο ουρανός σκοτείνιασε. Σύντομα χοντρές ψιχάλες χτυπούσαν δυνατά το τζάμι, καθώς το τρένο συνέχιζε τη διαδρομή του.

«Παππού, δεν μου αρέσει η βροχή», είπε με παράπονο το μικρό αγόρι. «Σκοτείνιασε. Δεν μπορώ να δω τίποτα!».

Η καταιγίδα χτυπούσε τώρα με ένταση το τζάμι του τρένου. Ο μικρός ήταν απελπισμένος, όλο νεύρα.

«Έλα να παίξουμε κάτι μαζί», τον παρακαλούσε ο παππούς. «Φέρε τις ζωγραφιές σου».

«Όχι, δεν θέλω. Εγώ θέλω να μπορώ να βλέπω έξω. Δεν μου αρέσει το μικρό δωμάτιο του τρένου. Είναι σκοτεινά», συνέχιζε γκρινιάζοντας.

«Ναι, αλλά με αυτό τον τρόπο θα φτάσουμε στους γονείς σου. Δεν είσαι χαρούμενος;».

«Όχι, σου λέω. Πώς θα περάσει η ώρα; Πού είμαστε;», έλεγε, κολλημένος στο τζάμι, καθώς προσπαθούσε να δει έξω.

Αποκαμωμένος να απαιτεί κάτι που δεν γινόταν, τον πήρε ο ύπνος στο κάθισμα του κουπέ του τρένου. Πέρασε αρκετή ώρα και κάποια στιγμή, ξυπνώντας, άνοιξε τα μάτια. Πρώτα το ένα, με θυμωμένο ακόμη ύφος κι έπειτα το άλλο. Η βροχή είχε σταματήσει. Έξω από το τζάμι η άκρη ενός ουράνιου τόξου έφτανε έως τις γραμμές του τρένου.

«Παππού, παππού, κοίτα πολλά χρώματα, σηκώθηκε φωνάζοντας ενθουσιασμένος. Μας ακολουθούν!».

«Ναι, αγόρι μου. Αυτά είναι τα χρώματα της ίριδας. Το λέμε ουράνιο τόξο!».

«Πού ήταν όλα αυτά τα χρώματα, παππού; Γιατί δεν τα βλέπαμε;»

«Εδώ ήταν πάντα, μικρέ μου. Χρειαζόταν, όμως, η βροχή για να τα δούμε. Είναι το φως που βγαίνει μέσα από τις σταγόνες του νερού».

«Πόσο όμορφα είναι, παππού».

Ο παππούς τον πήρε στην αγκαλιά του και τον κοίταξε στα μάτια. «Έτσι είναι και η ζωή μας, μικρέ μου πρίγκιπα. Σαν την διαδρομή του τρένου. Βλέπουμε ωραίες εικόνες, συναντάμε ανθρώπους και τοπία, μα δεν λείπουν και οι καταιγίδες. Ποτέ, όμως, να μη ξεχνάς ότι πάντα μετά την καταιγίδα έρχεται ένα ουράνιο τόξο. Και η ελπίδα επιστρέφει στη γη, σαν υπόσχεση για όλα τα καλά που μας περιμένουν!

«Ναι, κι εγώ σε λίγο θα είμαι στο σπίτι μου!» είπε ο μικρός χαρούμενα. «Σ' αγαπώ παππού!».

— **Ευνίκη Σαατσάκη**

Sea of Love — by Sabine Rixen, Netherlands

Ocean

Crossing the Ocean

On your way down the river of life
To the delta where the brown meets the blue
Be as vast, unlimited and bountiful as the ocean.
As you lap at the shore gently rocking with the breeze

Remember your power to rage
Be a whirlwind with your tempest.
You can be deep and calm,
Swelling and rolling with majestic wave
Or shallow and treacherous,
Ripping and foaming with tide
Recall your power of choice.
You can stretch forever,
Meet the sky at the horizon
And become the white clouds.

You can go to extremes,
Float around the planet
Frozen like a 'berg
But do not forget what joy
To melt and dissolve in the heat.

All these transformations are within your power.
Let go, trust in the one.
Be open to your destiny,
For an ocean refuses no river,
We are but sand tumbled on the beach.

— Michael de Glanville, Cyprus

Rainbow Dragon — Elena Gillespie, Scotland

A Greater Cause

As the people paused,
they were contributing to a greater cause.
Time and space opened for stillness,
compassion, and love.

Creative expression, faith, trust, and support -
These were foundational
as the people realized they are not alone.

There was room to breathe,
to connect, and to be.
Their spirit replenished.
Healing happened so naturally.

Out of the darkness and into the light,
an awakened world emerged -
United and in union with Mother Earth

— Dr. Jaena Stanley-Gonzaga, USA

Worth, Mojebu and the Is-ness

Once upon a time, in a galaxy far, far away there was the most beautiful planet named Worth. Worth was truly beautiful with its deep, clear blue oceans, fertile land, tall mountains, luscious rain forests, long rivers and deep lakes. It was a jewel of the cosmos. With no pollution on planet Worth, it was home to many exotic animals, fish and birds, as well as a special race of humans. The people were generally very loving and cared for each other with kindness and prided themselves on finding worth in all aspects of their lives. Although all those born on planet Worth understood what worth was, they were encouraged to find their worth and people were defined by the level of worth that they achieved. The more a person's worth, the more important they seemed to be, and people of great worth were held in very high esteem indeed. This did not mean that one person's worth was more valuable than the next persons, although this did create a divide within some communities. Life was generally good on planet Worth and the people tried

very hard to get along and not fight or bicker amongst each other, although that was not always possible, because the value of worth had become too important for some and so they lost their way in their understanding.

In one of the rural villages, lived a very handsome young man called Mojebu, he was athletic in build with dark wavy hair, bright blue eyes and a gentle smile. As he sat alone, Mojebu got to thinking, he'd noticed that although the people on planet Worth were basically happy, they always wanted more worth and even when they got more worth, there never seemed to be enough. This puzzled him and the more he looked the more he noticed this. Why was it never enough? What was it that was missing? These questions bothered Mojebu and given his desire to help, he decided that he would go off on a quest to find the answers.

It wasn't long before Mojebu packed a small backpack and set off. He vowed that he would travel far and wide until he found what he was looking for. He travelled to many a far land, over steep mountains and through deep valleys. On his long journey he came across many a wise man and woman, but his questions were still there, with no real answers. How can it be so elusive, he thought? Why, after all this time hasn't someone given me the answers? He began to wonder if he would ever find the answer to his questions. After travelling for many days, nights and years Mojebu began to tire, his spirit was low, and he was feeling very weary. He found himself sitting on a large rock at the entry to a quaint little village. He didn't know where he was, he had been walking for so long and through so many lands. As Mojebu sat resting, his eyes barely open, he could feel the presence of someone close by, he opened his eyes and there he saw a very old woman who appeared to be blind. She walked gently towards Mojebu, and sat down beside him. "Hello, young man" she said with a gentle voice; "what brings you to this village?" At first Mojebu thought he was seeing things, he shook his head and sheepishly looked at the old woman, "what... huh?" he responded as he gathered his thoughts. "I am on a quest to find the answer to a great question, but so far the answer alludes me". The woman turned toward him and although blind, it was as if she could see, she asked, "what is your question, young man?"

"Well" he said "the people of planet Worth are always trying to attain more worth, but no matter how hard they try and how much worth they attain, they never really feel happy inside themselves. I have travelled to many lands searching to find the reason for this and I have spoken to many wise people, but no one can satisfy me with the answer." The old woman's face lit up with a warm smile as she softly said, "young man you have just answered your question in a manner." "I have?" he questioned with a puzzled look. "yes" she said, the warmth exuding from her voice, "You see all this time you have been searching outwards to try and find the answer to your question, but as you just said, the people are inwardly unhappy, and when there is unhappiness inside, one tends to think the answer is outside of themselves. Begin your quest there, young man!" Mojebu had closed his eyes as the old lady was speaking and when he opened them, she was gone, poof into thin air as if she had never really been there at all. Mojebu scratched his head and looked around, "did I just dream this?" he asked himself "or was she real?". As he gathered his thoughts and remembered the wise words that had been gently spoken to him, he knew in his heart that his encounter with this old woman was real. The old woman's answer struck him so powerfully and he could see that all this time he had been looking outside of himself to find the answer and now, in one short moment the realisation had hit him. Why hadn't he looked inside? It was so obvious; how could he have missed this?

With new eyes and renewed vigour, he thought to himself "now finally I am on the right path". Mojebu paused for a moment and thought of the next steps he should take on his quest. He looked straight ahead and felt that there was a message in being right here, right now. It felt right for him to venture into the village, and as he walked around the village asking if there was a place to stay he also asked a few of the people if they knew the lady that had been talking to him outside the village. Nobody seemed to know who he was talking about, which he found quite odd, as he knew that she had been right there with him.

It wasn't long before one of the villagers offered him somewhere to stay. It was a quaint small cottage within the town and here he would make his new base from which to continue his search, only this time, instead of going far and wide, searching outside himself, he would instead start his search for the answer within, just like the old woman had said. There was a lovely old chair in a room with a view across the roofs of the village and beyond, to the valley and hilltops in the distance. He threw a thick old blanket on the chair, patted it into shape and hopped on to test it for comfort. After a few final adjustments it felt just right, so he got comfy and closed his eyes. He had no idea in his mind what this 'inner journey' would be like. He thought that by closing his eyes it would just happen.

Mojebu soon found that it wasn't what he 'thought' it would be. He was looking inside, but what was he looking for? All he found was lots of thoughts constantly bombarding him, he was thinking of what he might have for dinner, what he had done yesterday and the day before that, and his imagination was taking him to thoughts of tomorrow. He soon started to notice lots of little pains and niggles on his body, even the odd itch would come up, and try as he might, he just couldn't seem to keep his mind focused on his quest. This started to annoy him and fairly soon he found himself getting angry and frustrated. Why was this all so hard, he thought. He tried and tried and tried to focus his thoughts, but it seemed the harder he tried the harder it became to stay focused.

In pure frustration he jumped out of the chair saying out loud "I need to get out of here and get some clear air to calm my thoughts!" He stormed out of the cottage and then started wandering down the cobbled roadway until he happened upon the same large rock at the entry to the village.

He sat down holding his head in his hands, feeling very upset with himself, when he heard a familiar voice say, "Hello young man" a voice came from right next to him. He turned and there again was the old woman. "You seem troubled" she said in her soft, yet strong reassuring tone. "Yes, I am" he replied, "I have tried to look within for my answer, but all I found was noise, noise and more noise. My head just won't stop, and if it's not my thoughts it's my feelings and then I became angry and frustrated!"

"Oh" she said, followed by a very long pause. He looked at her and she continued, "Your answer lies in the Is-ness."

"The Is-ness?" he enquired

"Yes, the Is-ness, my dear young man." She paused again, "The Is-ness can't be found in the mind, nor in your memory nor your imagination, it's not in your feelings or your emotions either"

"Where can it be found then?" he asked.

"Ah not so fast" came her gentle reply, "you must first understand what the thoughts, feelings and emotions are."

He looked puzzled and thought to himself what is this old woman talking about? "Off course I know what they are." He blurted out.

The old woman took his hand in hers and with the gentlest of smiles said, "Look at your thoughts, have you ever found one that stays?"

"Stays?"

"Yes stays" she replied.

He thought about it for a moment and then turned his attention fully on his thoughts, they seemed to come and go all the time.

"Have you noticed" she said, "that no thought stays, and it's only the ones you grab hold of that you enlarge and build to create your own story?"

"My own story?" he questioned.

"Yes, your own story," she quietly replied, knowing that the young man was about to see something he had never noticed before. "Yes, thoughts come and go all the time, see them as clouds in the sky, they come and they go, some come and go fast, yet others seem to linger a little longer, but ultimately they all go. Focus on what remains when they are gone. If you look closely you will see it's not just your thoughts that come and go, but it's also your feelings and emotions too. Notice that nothing stays."

Mojebu pondered on the words and noticed that the old woman was right, his thoughts were in a sense just like clouds, in fact he tried very hard to see if any thought could stay, or if he had ever had a thought or feeling that had always been with him, and he found to his surprise that he couldn't find one. No matter how hard he tried, no thought would stay for more than a moment, all they did was to constantly change, but none stayed.

"Wow" he said "I never noticed that before"

The old woman smiled and continued "Yes, all people's lives are just a bundle of thoughts, feelings and emotions, coming and going, coming and going, even the people we meet constantly come and go. Have you noticed?"

"Yes you are right" he said with a look of deep contemplation on his forehead, "not even the people stay, they come and go in your life, some stay for a long time, but eventually they all go, or grow old and leave."

The old woman gave him a warm smile and continued "Now, through all of this, have you noticed anything that is always there?"

"Always there, what do you mean by this?" He questioned.

"Yes, there is something that never goes, look deeply within and you will see that everything is perceived by something that is always there. Look carefully and try to connect with it."

"Is that the Is-ness?" he asked turning his head so he could look straight at her.

"It's close" she smiled "But no, it's not the Is-ness, for that we must look a little deeper, but first look at the one thing we have discovered that is always there, it's what you call "I" but it's not what you see as your body or your mind. Because you can see it as though you were an observer, it can't be your body or mind, because they are both seen by it. Get to know it, watch it and see that it sees everything, but the "I" doesn't need to grab hold of any thought, any feeling or any emotion. Really get to know this. See that this "I" has always been known, and it appears changeless, it's as if it is watching and aware of you from the moment you first became aware, right through till now. Also notice that in all that time it never really changed. Stew on this and really get to see it clearly. In a way you could say it is the Knowing"

"But the Is-ness? What is the Is-ness?" Mojebu really wanted to know this now, what was the Is-ness?

"Ok" said the old woman, she knew he was ready and so she continued "The Is-ness is everything even beyond the knowing, but in order for the Is-ness to be there, you will need to disappear."

"Disappear!" Now Mojebu was puzzled, almost a little annoyed, "How will I know it, if I disappear, I won't even be there to know it!"

"Precisely!" exclaimed the old woman, "you, your body and mind won't

be there. Notice that you perceive everything, but are you actually what is perceived?" She paused "Are you,… really you?"

"What?" Mojebu seemed confused by these last words "Are you saying I'm not really here? I'm not this body, I'm not Mojebu?"

The old woman smiled, "Let's do a little exercise, this may help."

Mojebu eagerly said "Yes let's do it" he wanted to know the answer, no matter what it took, he just had to find it.

"Ok, first close your eyes" the old woman said, "now just relax everything, be aware of all the thoughts, feelings and emotions, but don't pick any of them up. Just let them drift on by, like clouds in the sky. Now imagine that in the bottom of one of your feet there is a hole. Now take all your thoughts, feelings, emotions, memories of the past, imaginings of the future and any idea that you have at all of you being someone. Let these all drain out of the hole in the bottom of your foot until you feel absolutely empty, not one thought, not one feeling, absolutely nothing left at all. Be totally empty, no identity, no ideas, absolutely nothing left."

Mojebu did as instructed and emptied himself of everything.

"Now what's left?" the old woman asked.

Mojebu looked, he couldn't find anything, it was completely empty, no shape, no Mojebu, no size, no thoughts, no feelings, just nothing, but strangely enough there was something, an awareness, kind of empty, yet not empty, and it felt incredibly good, an all-encompassing sensation of peace, ease, knowing and the sensation he was home and at rest.

"What do you see?" the old woman asked calmly, "Is there anything there? does it have any size, any shape, can you find where it starts, or finishes?"

To all these questions Mojebu could only say "No"

"Ok, did it come from anywhere, can it disappear?" She continued, "Can you feel sad there, can you be upset, or angry, does it belong to something or someone, can it be bought or sold?"

Again, all Mojebu could do, was say "No"

"How close is it to you?" she asked

"There is no distance" he replied

"This is the Is-ness" the warmth of the old woman's voice was apparent. "This is what we are all searching for, it's what we all long for."

"Yes" replied Mojebu, joy streaming from his being "and it's what we have always been, we've never been separate selves, we are all just one!"

The old woman tilted her head, "Yes, the Is-ness is just one, it is infinite. See how it is everything and nothing, all in the only moment there really is." And with those last words she dissolved right in front of Mojebu's eyes.

Mojebu rubbed his eyes, had it all been a dream of the old woman? It all appeared so real. He collected his thoughts and began to explore the meaning of what he had just encountered. He was the Is-ness, and now he could clearly see the answer to his question, not only this question, but it was as if there was nothing that he could not know. Everything was so clear, and he knew that it had always been clear, it's just that he had never seen it before. He pondered over what he had uncovered and now, he understood that his experience on planet Worth was a finite experience, one with boundaries, just like all the shapes of things on Worth. In fact, he realised that even the idea that he had of himself on Worth was just really another shape. All shapes had boundaries, they had limitations, like the outer skin of his perceived body, it had size and shape, and it was limited by that size and shape. He saw that all things on planet Worth were limited, they all had shape, they were objects, even his thoughts and emotions, they were all just shapes, and all shapes came and went, no shape was ever permanent, even planet Worth was a created shape and it too would disappear one day.

Then he looked at the Is-ness and saw it had no shape, it was shapeless with no boundaries, no beginning and no end, it was boundless and unlimited. Unlimited! Yes, absolutely unlimited! Knowing this, he could see that any limited experience was precisely that, limited! It came with limitations and that is why the people of planet Worth were never satisfied, because each experience they had carried limitation, and by that very nature, it was lacking, missing something, missing the no-thingness of the Is-ness. In the Is-ness everything was available, all could be experienced at once, with no distance, no time, no shapes, no limits at all! Everything was contained in the Is-ness, even the limited experience of planet Worth and all its people was contained in the Is-ness, nothing could, or would ever exist outside the Is-ness.

Mojebu now knew that all experiences would come and go and so all that was really required was to enjoy each experience as it arose, he didn't need to interfere, or create his own experience, with his thoughts or feelings or emotions, he could just relax and enjoy the show. In a sense he could sit back and enjoy the movie of his life, because essentially that was all it really was, a movie contained in the Is-ness. The Is-ness is the only truth, the only constant, all else is just a play within the Is-ness.

With his new understanding, Mojebu decided that all that was left for him to do now, was to go and share his discovery with all those who would listen to him, so he set off again to travel around planet Worth, this time to share with the outside world what he had uncovered on the inside.

— Marius Elder, Indonesia & Jacqui Land, UK

Holding a brown leaf — Ali Ford Photography, UK

A Love Letter To My Mother Gaia {Mother Earth}

You have provided me life, across the years, since my first breath did begin
Our spirits have touched I am sure and will again

Many people have you made whole
You have helped resolve their ills, issues of the soul

Although Your time of recovery, a new cycle begins
You are still helping others, you have so many friends

You have many friends to whom a debt they owe
Surely, as your body heals, your soul will know

Many are praying for your fast recovery and healing
So much work to do, yet it seems so appealing

For those of us who our mission we know
To help others succeed wherever we go

A tribute to you my Mother Earth, though we have never met,
Our souls have touched again, for this I have no regret

I leave you now, use your powers yet again
To heal thyself, be swift, and return to help all you call friend

— **Larry Mason**
3.15.2010 ... 6:04 pm:

Dear Gaia

What a great job you have done with the creation of the trees. I hope more people will celebrate their many splendors.

There are so many varieties. Some stay green all year like the coniferous ones, some bloom with flowers, some have needles, others leaves, and some even produce fruit that we can eat. I am grateful for fruit! The trees on our beautiful planet produce life-giving oxygen. It is so amazing that you created them so that one tree produces enough oxygen for two people to live an entire year!

I was pleasantly surprised to learn that trees reduce damage-causing flooding, and they also prevent soil erosion which in turn effects all else in nature. They provide cool shade to all creatures and plants when the sun is hot.

"trees" — Ali Ford Photography, UK

Then there is the interaction between the seasons and the trees. I love the Spring. This is the time of awakening. The long hibernation of nature has ended. The coniferous trees appear greener as new foliage appears. Other trees show signs of their awakening with buds and colourful blossoms. There is a quiet hum of anticipation as days become warmer. The rain also feels warm, and I feel you are celebrating the end of the quiet inward journey and sharing your transformation through your rain. It feels like a magical time as the new olive-coloured buds remind me of hope, possibility, and potential. What will transpire? How can I create beauty, a powerful loving space for all on the planet and…...? These are the questions that fill my mind and heart.

Spring leads us to Summer. As you may know, Gaia, I love the Summer. This is the time of year when the trees feel most vibrant. Branches are full of fresh green leaves, the colour of harmony and peace. It opens our hearts and helps us take long deep breaths. It is interesting that trees create oxygen and encourage us, with their waving leaves, to open our lungs and breathe deeply. It is in that deep breath that we find perfect peace and harmony where we can connect to our soul. If I feel like I need to be alone or I am having a bad day, I lie on the grass and watch the waving leaves and eventually drift into a land of dreams and desires, surrounded by the peace of green.

As days grow shorter, I am aware of the early morning coolness to the air. I see the leaves changing from their vibrant green to yellow with the arrival of Autumn. I feel you are reminding me that change will bring joy and that the sun still shines just as bright in the other seasons. Yellow leaves invite me to jump in a pile and throw them into the air.

When the air gets cooler in the early evenings with the sinking sun, you switch the leaves to the colour orange and invite me to experience bliss filled joy and feel your abundance…my abundance. Your change from orange to red absorbs any of the anger that I might feel as I am swept up in the change from Autumn to Winter. Winter feels so void of life. The trees look grey and sad yet accepting of the coming snow and ice as they stand still in surrender. They are great reminders to me that in stillness I can connect to my own inner journey and with faith know that potential filled Spring is just around the corner.

Thank you for all you do Gaia.

With Deep Love, Sacred Tree Woman

— **Susan McKenzie, Canada**

Gratitude: A Way of Life

Louise Hay always related gratitude to Thanking the Universe. Here's what Louise said about gratitude in her book Gratitude: A Way of Life:

Gratitude brings more to be grateful about. It increases your abundant life. Lack of gratitude, or complaining, brings little to rejoice about. Complainers always find that they have little good in their life, or they do not enjoy what they have. The Universe always gives us what we believe we deserve.

For quite some time now, I've been accepting every compliment and every present with "I accept with joy and pleasure and gratitude."

I have learned that the Universe loves this expression, and I constantly get the most wonderful presents.

When I awaken in the morning, the first thing I do before I even open my eyes is to thank my bed for a good night's sleep. I am grateful for the warmth and comfort it has given me.

From the beginning, it is easy to think of many, many more things I am grateful for. By the time I am out of bed, I have probably expressed gratitude for 80 or 100 different people, places, things, and experiences in my life. This is a great way to start the day.

— **Louise Hay**

*"It is not the JOY
that makes us grateful.
It is the GRATITUDE
that makes us joyful."*

— **David Steindl-Rast**

Multi-lingual Messages of Gratitude and Joy

*"Alegría; es lo que cada corazón necesita para ser feliz.
Joy; is what every heart needs to be happy."*

— **Pame Binninger, Mexico**

*Watashiwa shiyawase desu (Japanese)
I am joyful*

*Muzhe Anand hai (Indian)
I am in joy*

— **Rani Chainani, Japan**

*"Hoy, ayer y mañana…
Agradezco a mis padres por la vida.
Agradezco a mi familia por permitirme ser quien soy hoy.
Agradezco a mi luz interior por mis ganas de siempre dar y recibir con amor.
Agradezco a mi inquieto corazón por permanentemente ser mi guía.
Agradezco a mis ojos por constantemente ver lo mejor en otros y en mi.
Agradezco a mi alma por enseñarme el camino.
Agradezco a mi voz interior por hacerse escuchar.
Agradezco al Universo porque estoy exactamente donde debería estar y
por sobre todo, por ser consciente y confiar.
Agradezco a mi pasado, a mi presente y a mi futuro por tanto.
Agradezco por ser el mejor reflejo de quien lee esta nota.
Hoy, ayer y mañana agradezco por ti y por tu vida."*

— **Delia C. O. Sanchez, UK**

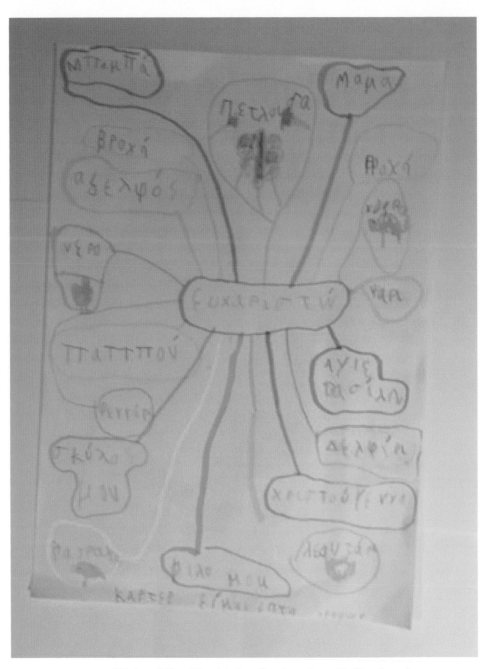

— Web of Gratitude, by Carter, Age 7, England
(Learner of Greek since September 2019)

"Είμαι ευγνώμων για:

την αγάπη, την ζεστασιά και την υποστήριξη της οικογένειας και φίλων, μια στέγη πάνω από το κεφάλι μου και ζεστό σπίτι,

τις δωρεά μικρές απολαύσεις της ζωής, όπως ηλιοβασιλέματα, Ανατολή, περπάτημα στην παλιά και στους βουνά.

Η υπομονή του δασκάλου μου Χρυσουλα που προσπάθησε να με διδάξει αυτή την όμορφη γλώσσα.

Η γενναιοδωρία των ανθρώπων που δεν έχω γνωρίσει ποτέ.

Η μεγαλύτερη μου χαρά είναι να ζήσω μια ευτυχισμένη και εκπληκτική ζωή."

— Ruth Sadik, England (Learner of Greek since September 2019)

Με λένε Κεν. Είμαι εβδομήντα χρονών. Είμαι πολύ τυχερός γιατι έχω μια υπέροχη ζωή. Είμαι ευγνώμων για τους γονείς μου, την γυναίκα μου, τους δύο γιους μου και τους φίλους μου εγώ λέω "ευχαριστώ." Αν και οι ευχαριστίες δεν είναι αρκετές.

Ken Sterling
Shropshire. U.K.

Fimleikar!

Eitt af því skemmtilegasta sem við gerum er að æfa fimleika. Það er góður félagsskapur og við eigum marga vini þar. Þjálfararnir eru skemmtilegir, góðar fyrirmyndir og þjálfa okkur vel. Við höfum lært mörg trix og erum alltaf að læra eitthvað nýtt. Það sem er svo skemmtilegt við fimleika er að þú ert alltaf að takast á við nýjar áskoranir. Stökkin verða stærri og trixin verða flóknari. Þú getur alltaf bætt þig í því sem þú ert að æfa og það finnst okkur gaman. ☺

Gymnastics!

One of the things that brings us the most joy, is practicing gymnastics. We are in really good company and have many friends there. The coaches are fun, good role models and they train us well. We have learned many skills and tricks and we keep learning new things. The fun thing about gymnastics is that you keep getting new challenges. The jumps become bigger and higher and the moves become more complicated. There is always room for improvement and that is what we like. ☺

— **Lilja Karítas 12 yrs & Katrín Líf 10 yrs, Iceland**

Owning what has always been mine

What would it be to accept the crossing of our two paths?
An incident so normal on any day of this magic Earth.
Breathing naturally without yearning for more,
Simply conscious and without expectation.

Soaked in the clarity of happiness
Feeling the pull towards situations that generate bliss.
The choice inevitably leaves me vulnerable, defenceless,
Grateful and ready for meetings of this kind.

For the joy is already within me,
The love that fills this strong heart, truly mine.
It is I who is aware of this bliss.

Every day as we spin around our star
If I will listen, if I care to hear,
The enchanting song of this life awaits me.

— Michael de Glanville, Cyprus

Dear Mother Earth

I'm writing you this letter to let you know how much you have meant to me over the years. When I was a toddler, I remember sitting on your sandy beaches at our family cabin where I loved to play for hours. As I grew older, my mom and my maternal grandparents would walk your beaches and gather treasures that washed upon your shores. The adults would find agates and my mom would circle ones for me to 'find on my own'. We spent countless hours fishing and gathering the bounty you generously offered.

When I was eight and my home wasn't always a safe place to be, I would run out into your woods and lay on your soft forest floor and look up into the canopy of your trees. As they swayed back and forth with the wind, I would feel Father sky looking down on me and I felt the rhythm on your maternal heartbeat. I felt safe and connected like no other place. You became my 'house of worship' and my sanctuary in time of trouble. As I grew older and my home became even more dangerous, I would run across your grass and climb to the top of the tallest tree because my pursuer was afraid of heights. I would feel the wind upon my face and Father sky assured me that all would be well.

"water" — Ali Ford Photography

Building a dam in your creeks with my bare feet and hands absorbed all of life's troubles.

In my teens, I rode horses and dirt bikes to Whistle Lake and camped for days without another soul to threaten me. I had numerous off-road vehicles for the 'soul' purpose of connecting with you, and I always did. You were always there for me.

When I had children of my own, it was our tradition to go into your forest and connect with each other through you. We went back to that family cabin on the beach and pass on your rich traditions. All of my 8 children and all of 7 of my grandchildren feel and appreciate you.

When my youngest child was diagnosed with Leukemia, I returned to you the first chance I got to find that connection we always shared and ask Father sky why. When he was too immune suppressed to touch your soil, I would lay in the grass on my back with him laying on top of me chest to chest so that our heartbeats became one. So he would be connected to you through me. It gave him calm in a way nothing else would. When he finally was given permission, we would lay in that same position, but he was able to lay his hands and bare feet directly on you to help dissipate the energy of the hospital and the brutal treatment the way I had as a boy. When he was finally given clearance to travel, we went straight to the family cabin as we had visualized so many times while isolated in the confines of the hospital. We always looked forward to our return to your grounding healing energy.

He is amazingly healthy, and you are a major part of his recovery.

We will spend the rest of our lives in gratitude of you always being there for us and we vow to return the kindness.

— **Jeffrey Granville, USA**

Rainbow Recipe for Joy

1 cup of smiles
1 cup of laughter
1 cup of love
1 cup of gratitude
1 cup of peace
1 cup of patience

Mix all together with the help of your Angels

To the right of you place the Angel of patience

To the left of you place the Angel of peace

Behind you place the Angel of love

In front of you place the Angel of gratitude

Above you place the Angel of smiles

Below you place the Angel of laughter

Now breathe for 5 minutes, long, slow, deep breaths.

Add some sunshine until you are ready, then have a slice each day.

To bring in more Joy.

— Elspeth Kerr, Cyprus

Inner Guide — by Sabine Rixen, Netherlands

Your powerful inner light

The simple things
The simple experience
The presence
Easy – presence - silence
The simple life – natural life – mindful life
Everything becomes uncomplicated when you are present

In the present - you will find joy, loving and caring

Presence provides joy and inner peace
Presence is love
Love is everything

Everything is energy
Light is energy
Joy is energy

Faces smiling in the light
To each other
For you
To me
You are your own inner light
The light gives you a feeling of joy and embraces life and love
Love embraces your soul and lets your inner light sing and smile

Your inner light warms your own heart and every heart in the Universe
It's uncomplicated when you are – just are
You are light - and shinning
Light up for yourself and everybody
Keep shining

— **Lene Kirk, Denmark**

Cosmic Connections

As I connect to the Stars in the beautiful night sky, I see how lucky we all are to be living here on Mother Earth. The MOON with her changing phases, so beautiful when full, looks down on us at night, and feels like an old friend who is always there for us. We never feel alone when we look up at all the stars in the sky at night, and we feel a deep connection to the cosmos. I remember doing this as a child in my Grandad's garden, lying on the grass looking up at all the stars and the constellations. It is a memory that has stayed with me all my life. A sense of wonder filled me about our connection with the stars.

All the planets in the Cosmos interact with us through our Astrology Birth Chart. Each one making connections that create a unique blueprint for each one of us.

The SUN lights up the sky during the day, brings us warmth, and enables us to survive on planet Earth. The Sun in your Astrology Chart shows how and where you like to shine your light, and what element you express your energy through. The energy of your Sun Sign needs to be expressed so that you feel alive. The Sun is Creative energy and the Moon is Receptive energy.

The Sun brings heat to the earth and helps all the trees, plants and vegetables to grow. We are thankful for the food that we eat which is grown in Mother Earth.

We are blessed in so many ways to be living on this beautiful planet Earth. We have the Blue Oceans, bringing us a sense of calm, peace and tranquillity. We have the Green Forests, bringing us a feeling of being Grounded and Connected with Mother Nature. We feel rejuvenated when we spend time walking in nature, and also when walking by the ocean. These are free to us from Mother Earth, and are essential for our wellbeing. We are so lucky to have them. We can connect even more with the Water element by swimming in the sea. Deep in the oceans we have all the beautiful mammals who live there and who also need to be protected, the beautiful Dolphins, sharks and lots of other sea life. We need to be mindful of keeping our seas clean so that the sea life can continue to swim freely in the oceans.

I am grateful to Mother Earth for growing the food that we eat, and giving us water to drink. The Air that we breathe is all around us, invisible to the eye but essential to living on planet Earth. When we feel stressed, we can take some deep breaths to help us to slow down and enjoy the natural world we all live in. We must appreciate all that Mother Nature has to offer us, and in return send her love, and help to keep her in balance.

Mother Earth has given us lots of beautiful animals to keep us company too. Many people have cats and dogs as pets which bring a lot of love into people's lives. Mother Earth has an Abundant energy, always growing, and bringing us the changing seasons, and all the beautiful flowers for each one. The seasons give us a sense of change and also beginnings and endings. Spring brings a feeling of freshness and new beginnings. The leaves are beginning to grow on the trees. Summer brings a feeling of warmth and happiness, and we feel more carefree when the Sun is shining.

The Autumn brings a feeling of change, as we move into the colder months and the leaves fall from the trees. The Autumnal colours are amazing with combinations of oranges, yellows and browns and reds. It brings a feeling of going inward, as we move towards the Winter season which can be a time of hibernation for a lot of animals, and life can seem that it is standing still at times. Then the cycle begins again when we welcome the season of Spring, as we spring into Action for the beginning of a whole new cycle.

The Spring Equinox is the beginning of the Astrological New Year, when the Sun enters the sign of Aries, which is an action sign and ruled by the planet Mars, an action planet, and so very apt for Spring, and also emphasising the connection we have here on planet Earth with the Cosmos and the movement of the planets and the changing of the seasons.

The Earth, our home planet, is a world unlike any other, it is very beautiful and is the third planet from the Sun, and is the only known place in the universe to host life. It is located in one of the spiral arms of the Milky Way (the Orion arm). Our Sun is one Star among the billions in the Milky Way Galaxy. You might like to take some time to stand outside on a clear night and feel the connection with your Cosmic Family.

I am visualising a beautiful big Rainbow Heart of Love sinking down into the ground and deep into Mother Earth to let her know how much we love her.

— **Ruth McCarthy, Republic of Ireland**

Goddess from Epona

Let yourself be so free
like Noreen's horses can be,
Living in a precious land,
Hidden in the beautiful nature of Ireland.

They run freely on the sparkling field of green soaked imagination,
Appreciating their presence on the Planet Earth
In the secret place called Epona.
They are amazing gentle creatures, called Ruby, Lizzie and Isabel.

No, this wasn't in my dream!
This place belongs to a daydreaming land of everlasting greenery that
brings calmness to your heart and fulfils your soul, with peace.
Yes, you and me, we can experience its beauty gracefully, when the
right time comes.

Let your hair down, whilst touching Lizzie's body of golden energy
turned into the shape of that magnificent horse she's become now after
being a unicorn, once upon a time.

How do I know that?
She has the most beautiful blonde fringe on the whole planet, and the
eyes of Goddess.
Look at those eyes!
You can see the Universe in them gazing at you with cosmic love, sent
by higher beings to help humans.
Connect, breath and feel it!
The healing message that has been delivered to your doorsteps.

— **Mira Warszawski, UK**

My A-Z of JOY

Life can throw us so many curve balls, and often they turn out to be just the wakeup call we needed. Everything truly does happen for a reason.

In 2011 my life came crashing down; literally. I fell down the stairs head first and put my head through the wall. I was lucky to be alive!

Before my fall I would probably argue it "impossible" to take time for myself. I felt like I was soooooo busy. But life found a way to prove me wrong and put me back on track.

It took many months to recover. It forced me to slow down. It made me think about what I truly wanted from life. If I'd been given a second chance, I needed to take it!

But when I considered the question "What do I want?" it seemed so hard to answer. My brain struggled to find THE answer.

So, I developed this exercise that I have returned to and shared many times over.

I invite you to complete the table considering what would spark your JOY, and make you feel alive and lit up?

Don't censor the answers, just listen to the whispers of your soul.

There's no right or wrong answer, only what feels good to you.

It might take you an hour to complete, a day, a week or even a month.

Give yourself permission to get that clarity. As the saying goes, you get what you focus on. (I don't recommend you focus on being busy that's for sure, or you might find life has a way to give you a wakeup call!)

To help you complete the table, you might want to envisage your ideal day, or cast your mind back to favourite memories that you'd love to re-create.

Nothing is too small; it might be as simple as lighting your candles each night or planting an apple tree, or simply smiling. But likewise, nothing is too big, just allow yourself to record your soul's desires.

Once you've completed it, you might start to notice that you're saying the same things in different ways, so clearly your soul is calling for your attention on these things.

And of course, once you have your A-Z of JOY, it's time to act upon each spark and bring you vision to life!

All the things I want to Be, Do and Have
to spark my JOY and make me feel alive and lit up.

— **Debbie Hayes, UK**

	BE	DO	HAVE
A			
B			
C			
D			
E			
F			
H			
I			
J			
K			
L			
M			
N			
O			
P			
Q			
R			
S			
T			
U			
V			
W			
X			
Y			
Z			

Resources

Our Resources section is available on our website **www.rainbowletterstomotherearth.com** where you'll find a range of educational and practical resources to help families, children, young people and anyone navigating waves of uncertainty, loss, grief, anxiety and sadness whether caused by the unprecedented crisis of the pandemic or a different type of crisis or change as we go through life.

We're excited to include inspirational tools to support all our readers wholistically for your mental, emotional, physical and spiritual health and wellbeing:

- recommendations of books
- collection of meditations
- music, audio files, interviews, blog articles
- videos of panel discussions taken during the "Be Kind To Your Mind! Summit"
- guidance and inspiration to find joy through creativity e.g. create your own notebook or start a new hobby like painting
- *"sparks of joy"* in the form of tips and techniques to bring into your everyday life irrespective of age, gender, ethnicity etc.

ONLINE COURSES

Online Courses for children and young people
Online Courses for Parents

- Introduction to Colour Psychology and Colour Therapy
- The 7-Step RAINBOW Method
- The RAINBOW Bears and The 7 Cs / the 7 Seas
- The Truth About Dragons: Introduction to the Celestial Guardians

To Sleep or not to Sleep: **The Benefits of Sleeping Well** and how it helps with our mood and increase levels of joy. Full article by Constance Schaap, Netherlands

Open Eye Reading Meditation: Use your Mind to find Joy by Elspeth Kerr, Cyprus

Healing Love Tool by Lars Heiselberg Vang Jensen, Denmark

World Kindness Matters Challenge - for families and schools - Whole School Event Completing Acts of Kindness

The Hierarchy of Feelings: Aiming for Joy by ChriSOULa Sirigou

Mountains of Great Ideas Notebook by Lene Nielsen - watch the **video recording** of the "Mountains of Great Ideas" workshop organised by RAINBOW Letters to Mother Earth on 10.10.20 in support of World Mental Health Day in our Facebook page here: **https://fb.watch/2bxyq6VP6J** or on our RAINBOW Letters to Mother Earth YouTube Channel.

The Embrace — Sabine Rixen, Netherlands

THE MIRACLE OF YOU" From Album: "Miracle of You" Music & Lyrics By Paul Luftenegger © 2015 All Rights Reserved

In Partnership with New York Times Best Selling Author Anita Moorjani Inspired By Anita Moorjani's Life & Best Selling Book "Dying To Be Me"

Performed at the United Nations Headquarters in New York City in 2017 Sharing the Stage with Dr. Bruce Lipton PhD & Sister Shivani of the Brahma Kumaris of India – And Paul Luftenegger's Album Used By Anita Moorjani In Her Workshops and Lectures Around The World.

Come take a ride with me to paradise
Heaven is in your heart beating inside
You're alive
The great divine
Older than time
You are loved
Yes you are loved

And the stars in our sky
Billion year old lights light up the sky
And you can feel the Universe through your heart
The divine design of you
The time has come for you
To honour the miracle of you

And you are so beautiful
The way your body moves and holds it all
Your heart lights up hearts
And your love illuminates our world
Your soul is old
Your soul is old

And the stars in our sky
Billion year old lights light up the sky
And you can feel the Universe through your heart
The divine design of you
The time has come for you
To honour the miracle of you

Oh the roads been long
And the heart is strong
Let your love lift you up
Let your heart rocket you
To honour the miracle of you

Epilogue

The greatest challenge in this LIFE is to find a way to keep your heart open through the extremes and acknowledge the little sparks of joy presented to you.

It's the extremes of LIFE that spur us into action the most. Through staying open to these extremes, we're able to experience LIFE fully. Death gives way to birth, grief gives way to healing, separation gives way to union, resentment gives way to forgiveness — on and on it goes.

When we zoom out, it's possible to gain a greater perspective. Then we

"be love where we are" — K8 the heARTist, USA

realise the breathtaking beauty of this planet that so much of humanity has taken for granted.

The answer isn't to ignore the devastation that's happening here. Nor is it to ignore the interconnectedness of it all. Just as we can't heal what we don't acknowledge in our own life, the same goes for us as a planet. I trust in nature's ability to regenerate. I believe that this planet can do that too, and we can do that too — but it will require us to stop seeing ourselves as separate from nature.

Each of us can be, if we allow it, part of nature's great regeneration.

Each of us can be, if we allow it, part of the reweaving of the fabric of LIFE here on planet Earth.

Why have I chosen the Northern Lights or Aurora Borealis illustration as part of the cover of Little Sparks of Joy book (as I did with my first award-winning anthology)? I've chosen it, because it ignites joy and childlike wonder in my whole being, and because this book is dedicated to all of you joy bringers and light bearers.

It serves as a reminder to us all to raise our gaze to see the mystery that's woven through it all. When this mesmerising, awe-inspiring, playful dance of colour, stardust and light unexpectedly gives its performance through the darkness in the skies, it is an act of blissful joy. This is worth embracing with a sparkle in our eyes and gratitude in our hearts, for the wonder and beauty of the Universe and Mother Earth.

The RAINBOW … also does exactly that! On our way to Scotland for a short break after the passing of my father-in-law and with my heart filled with grief and sadness, we saw three wonderful rainbows, one after the other, welcoming us and reminding us that life is beautiful even when we experience unprecedented extremes like the pandemic. During this two-day escape (literally as the isolation was being imposed again), I opened my heart to inspiration and the concept of the book was born.

If you'd like to know more about the elders contributing in this book, many have their own websites. Search online for more details. Equally, you can join our newsletter on our website **www.rainbowletterstomotherearth.com** and connect with the contributing authors, poets and artists and our sponsors.

May the words, the lyrics, the colours, the sounds, the smells, the images and the emotions emanating from each "RAINBOW Letter" in this book, keep our hearts open to ourselves, Mother Earth, and each other.

May we continue to do what we can to preserve children's innocence by remembering our own. May we continue to play our part, in our own small way, in the great orchestra of LIFE through inspired, grounded action and by spreading Little Sparks of Joy.

Be a Spark of Joy! Express your SOUL. Let yourself be seen and call your RAINBOW Warriors home to you.

ChriSOULa
November 2021

About ChriSOULa

ChriSOULa Sirigou is a writer, teacher, visionary, creative, intuitive numerologist and colour psychologist specialising in the energy system of Colour Mirrors. She is currently living in Nantwich, England and is originally from the sunny shores of Athens, Greece. All of her creations are dedicated to giving young people and adults an experience of their own unique colours.

As a young child ChriSOULa displayed a unique fascination with self expression, sensitivity and the inner life. She experienced communicating her feelings and emotions through letter writing as a teenager and has been studying the power of the heart ever since.

She has already published an award-winning anthology book in colour, The Book of Soulful Musings. ChriSOULa teaches in person and virtually across the globe. Her work helps people to remember that they are part of nature, and to connect with the wisdom of the soul, and live in alignment with that.

Through her work, ChriSOULa guides us to connect to the RAINBOW Warrior within and to turn our soul's whispers into inspired action. Her work is inclusive, empowering, activating, and initiatory. Her pioneering Wholistic Love educational programmes and 7-Step RAINBOW Method benefit schools and families.

ChriSOULa's mission is to weave wonder and creative joy into our relationships and creative expressions on Mother Earth, and to help us unite with compassion and love.

www.chrisoulasirigou.com

www.wholisticlove.org.uk

www.rainbowletterstomotherearth.com

Acknowledgements

To the team at RAINBOW Letters to Mother Earth thank you for your wisdom, guidance and support. To all the sponsors and contributors, we are grateful for your response with generosity, enthusiasm, belief and trust.

We would also like to express our thanks to K8 the heARTist for giving permission to include her "Mama Earth" artwork on the cover of Little Sparks of Joy, including Elena Gillespie, Sabine Rixen and Anna Sophia for their pieces of Artwork in the book, images from Golden Lee in Mojebu story as well as Ali Ford Photography for the inclusion of her photos.

Thanks to the following people who have helped bring Little Sparks of Joy to life, both as a collection and as a new podcast platform for children, young people and those who care for them.

Alex Juul Nielsen	Denmark
Ali Ford	UK
Anastasia Nikopoulou	Greece
Anna Sophia	Netherlands
Annemieke Hebenaar	Netherlands
Aurelia Rasmussen	Denmark
Ashildur Hlin Valtysdottir	Iceland
Benedicte Holmbo Brandt	Denmark
Bruce Cryer	USA
ChriSOULa Sirigou	UK
Constance Schaap	Netherlands
Debbie Hayes	UK
Delia Sanchez	UK
Elena Gillespie	Scotland
Elspeth Kerr	Cyprus
Evniki Saatsaki	Greece
Filippa - Nature Lover	Denmark
Gabriele Wolter	Scotland
Gaja Lesiak	UK
Gina Theofilidou	Greece
Gitte Winter Graugaard	Denmark
Golden Lee	Indonesia
Hayley Lawson	UK
Hilda Rendl	Canada
Ilona Parunakova	USA

Ioannis Mintsidis	Greece
Jacqui Land Keavney	UK
Jaena Stanley-Gonzaga	USA
Jeffrey Granville	USA
Jessycka Drew Colours	USA
Karen Shaw	UK
Kasey Gloer	USA
K8 the heARTist Kate Lumley	USA
Katrin Lif	Iceland
Ken Sterling	UK
Khalida Nur van Helden	Indonesia
Larry Mason	USA
Lars Heiselberg Vang Jensen	Denmark
Lene Kirk	Denmark
Lene Nielsen	Denmark
Lilja Karitas	Iceland
Lotte Cecilie Juel Pedersen	Denmark
Maria Sirigou	Greece
Marius	Indonesia
Maureen Brindle	UK
Melina Tsoleridou	Greece
Michael de Glanville	Cyprus
Mira Warszawski	UK
Naomi Victoria Gilmour	UK
Noreen O'Neill Roche	Republic of Ireland
Pame Binninger	Mexico
Paul Luftenegger	Canada
Pauline Gallagher	Cyprus
Payal Irani	India
Rani Chainani	Japan
Richard Dubrick	USA
Ruth McCarthy	Republic of Ireland
Ruth Sadik	UK
Sabine Rixen	Netherlands
Samantha Houghton	UK
Sandy Summers	Scotland
Sharon Mundy	USA
Sean McCarthy	UK
Sherry Brouzes	Canada
Susan Brookes-Morris	UK
Susan McKenzie	Canada
Theonymfi Tachopoulou	Greece
Viola Edward de Glanville	Cyprus

Picture and Image Credits

Alex Juul Nielsen   p. 28, 29

Ali Ford Photography   p. 14, 16, 30, 38, 70, 72,
                                           80, 85, 88, 92, 99

Anna Sophia   p. 20, 21, 26

Carter Whitlow   p. 76

Elena Gillespie   p. 60

Filippa, Nature lover   p. 51

Jessycka Drew Colors   p. 24

Kate Lumley, K8 the heARTist   p. 6, 20, 96

Khalida Nur van Helden   p. 45

Sabine Rixen   p.10, 36, 58, 83, 94

Sharon Mundy   p. 32

Golden Lee   p. 62, 67

Images in At the Edge of the Rainbow Στην άκρη του ουράνιου τόξου by 10-year old children from Koufalia, Thessaloniki, Greece

Sunshine by Ioannis Mintsidis / Ιωάννης Μηντσίδης   p. 53
Rain by Anastasia Nikopoulou / Αναστασία Νικοπούλου   p. 54
Rainbow by Melina Tsoleridou / Μελίνα Τσολερίδου   p. 56

What next?

RAINBOW Letters to Mother Earth
Subscribe on our newsletter
www.rainbowletterstomotherearth.com

Follow us on Facebook
YouTube Channel
Podcast "Little Sparks of Joy"

Book Publication by ChriSOULa Sirigou
Award-winning The Book of Soulful Musings:
Inspiring Conversations to Live LIFE

with Love Intention Flow Ease

Get Creative

**Share these RAINBOW Letters and keep writing your own.
Make your voices heard; *Ignite Little Sparks of Joy.***

We encourage you to:

Write

A RAINBOW Letter is open to interpretation. It can be a poem, spoken word, a performance, a drawing, an artwork, a song, a dance. What creative form gives expression to what you want to say?

Organise

Can you organise a letter-writing or reading event in your workplace, school or community where you can present your RAINBOW Letter to spark conversation between people?

Share

We are gathering your messages, visions and dreams for a better world and making sure they are seen and heard.
In writing and sharing these RAINBOW Letters with others, new conversations and new possibilities can emerge.
Share it on social media using **#RainbowLetterstoMotherEarth**
@rainbowletterstomotherearth
Let this book be something you can fall back onto, whenever your SOUL needs nourishment and to tap into sources of hope, joy and inspiration.

For further information about our people-powered, community-serving campaigns and resources about RAINBOW Letters to Mother Earth Project:

www.rainbowletterstomotherearth.com

Find us on Facebook, Instagram, YouTube, Soundcloud
Our new **Podcast** channel provides a platform for children, parents and change makers from all over the world to share their voices.

Write your RAINBOW Letter

Testimonials & Endorsements

As soon as I opened the book and read the Foreword by the luminous Paul Luftenegger and then was treated to a gallery of magnificent nature photography and sweet drawings and elegant paintings of Mother Earth, and then as I read the touching letters from children as well as adults, I had become mesmerized. And inspired. And impassioned to help our Mother like never before. Little Sparks of Joy is a miraculous gift to humanity right now as our Mother makes clear her pain at the hands of her Children. This book is magnificent and tender and sublime and sweet and all the qualities humanity needs to return to our beloved Mother. Thank you for this magnificence.

— **Bruce Cryer, former CEO and co-creator of HeartMath, founder of Renaissance Human**

Little Sparks of Joy truly inspires people to make a difference by bringing hope and something valuable to ignite us to change our life and life on Mother Earth for the better. Inspirational, motivational and empowering!

— **Ilona Parunakova, Best-Selling Author, TEDx Speaker, Founder and CEO of IP Resilience Global Magazine**

ChriSOULa has created the most loving space for daring and sharing from our heart, listening to ourselves is a magnificent art.

The Little Sparks of Joy has even before publication inspired, ignited, and illuminated creativity by children of all ages and in all colours of the Rainbow. Let's explore what else is possible when we journey onwards - enriched with this magical publication and each contributor's special message in our hearts.

With love, gratitude and twinkles in my eyes

— **Lene Nielsen, founder of How Heart Can It Be?**

Little Sparks of Joy gives adults & children all over the world the opportunity to express their love through painting and writing beautiful poetry to Mother Earth with the strengths they have inside. So blessed to have an amazing poem written about my 3 therapy horses in your book. A beautiful book full of Peace & Love for one true self and Mother Earth. Thank you ChriSOULa, cherished with love.

— Noreen Roche, Epona Retreat Centre

Little Sparks of Joy is such a heart warming book project led by the amazing golden muse ChriSOULa Sirigou, who has my deepest respect. By uniting children, light workers and artists across the globe she brings hope to the future generation. With so much focus on the current climate crisis, it is important to also bring hope, light and love into play. I honor the contributors and the creators of this little pearl and wish for it to bring joy to the readers. Being part of the "Rainbow Letters to Mother Earth" community is a joy to me and makes me believe that together we can make a difference. Come join us."

— Bestselling author Gitte Winter Graugaard

Little Sparks of Joy is a really good book with good thoughts beautifully expressed - a truly magical experience.

Even more amazing is the fact that these thoughts are those experienced and shared by young children. These vivid chapters will open up your mind and melt your heart and bring joy in your life. Read it in a quiet place with the openness of a child's heart and be prepared to be amazed.

You will feel the joy that comes from watching a sparkler in your hand alight and throw out scintillate of sparks at India's Diwali festival (which is when I read it in Mumbai).

The neurons in my head seemed to buzz and sparkle as a I got to look at so many issues from a child's point of view. I realized that this goes beyond a child's or even an adult's purity of wisdom that can come from the unsullied hearts and out of the mouths of babes.

ChriSOULa Sirigou has done a marvelous job of collating these contributions from kids around the world. Children's libraries globally should keep a copy so that little visitors can enjoy the diversity of expression from other kids their own age. It will do a great deal for encouraging an openness to other cultures, because wherever they are, the challenges and thoughts of kids run along the same wavelength.

One hopes for another similar compilation to follow this one.

- Payal Irani, Founder and CEO
of Bloom Transformations Together

Printed in Poland
by Amazon Fulfillment
Poland Sp. z o.o., Wrocław